Appointing a Quantity Surveyor

A Guide

With Form of ment
and Terms of

THE ROYAL
INSTITUTION
OF CHARTERED
SURVEYORS

Appointing a Quantity Surveyor: A Guide for Clients and Surveyors
was originally published by RICS Books as three separate titles:

- *Client Guide to the Appointment of a Quantity Surveyor* First Edition (February 1992)

- *Form of Enquiry and Fee Quotation for the Appointment of a Quantity Surveyor*
  First Edition (February 1992)

- *Form of Agreement, Terms and Conditions for the Appointment of a Quantity Surveyor*
  First Edition (February 1992)

Contracts (Rights of Third Parties) Act 1999

Subsequent to the coming in force on 11 November 1999 of the Contracts (Rights of Third
Parties) Act 1999 (c. 31), third party rights have not been covered in this document.

For coverage of the Contracts (Rights of Third Parties) Act 1999, the reader is referred to
A. Day, P. Moore and G. Murphy, *Deeds of Collateral warranty and the Contracts (Third Party
Rights) Act 1999* (June 2000), published by RICS Books.

Please note: References to the masculine include,
where appropriate, the feminine

Published by RICS Business Services Limited
a wholly owned subsidiary of
The Royal Institution of Chartered Surveyors
under the RICS Books imprint
Surveyor Court
Westwood Business Park
Coventry
CV4 8JE

No responsibility for loss occasioned to any person
acting or refraining from action as a result of the
material included in this publication can be accepted
by the author or publisher.

ISBN 0 85406 926 7

Reprinted 2001

Printed by Newnorth Print Ltd, Bedford

Contents

RICS Guidance Notes

This is a Guidance Note. It provides advice to Members of the RICS on aspects of the profession. Where procedures are recommended for specific professional tasks, these are intended to embody 'best practice', i.e. procedures which in the opinion of the RICS meet a high standard of professional competence.

Members are not required to follow the advice and recommendations contained in the Note. They should however note the following points.

When an allegation of professional negligence is made against a surveyor, the Court is likely to take account of the contents of any relevant Guidance Notes published by the RICS in deciding whether or not the surveyor had acted with reasonable competence.

In the opinion of the RICS, a Member conforming to the practices recommended in this Note should have at least a partial defence to an allegation of negligence by virtue of having followed those practices. However, Members have the responsibility of deciding when it is appropriate to follow the guidance. If it is followed in an appropriate case, the Member will not be exonerated merely because the recommendations were found in an RICS Guidance Note.

On the other hand, it does not follow that a Member will be adjudged negligent if he has not followed the practices recommended in this Note. It is for each individual surveyor to decide on the appropriate procedure to follow in any professional task. However, where Members depart from the practice recommended in this Note, they should do so only for good reason. In the event of litigation, the Court may require them to explain why they decided not to adopt the recommended practice.

In addition, Guidance Notes are relevant to professional competence in that each surveyor should be up to date and should have informed himself of Guidance Notes within a reasonable time of their promulgation.

Selection and Appointment Advice

Selection and Appointment Advice

This Section outlines for Clients and Surveyors when and how to select and appoint a Quantity Surveyor.

1.   Introduction

1.1   The Royal Institution of Chartered Surveyors ('the RICS') has published this Guide to assist Clients when they wish to appoint a chartered Quantity Surveyor. The contents of the Guide should also assist Quantity Surveyors when concluding an agreement with their Client.

1.2   Over the last few years changes have taken place in the market place for professional services. Consultants are now appointed less often by reputation and recommendation and more often after a process of competition. Competition takes place in the private and public sectors and is supported by European Union requirements and UK Compulsory Competitive Tendering legislation.

1.3   This Guide is applicable to a range of situations – whether details of the services required are proposed to or by the Quantity Surveyor, or whether appointment is of a single Quantity Surveyor or following selection from a limited list. The Guide sets out principles to be considered and applied rather than a detailed step-by-step procedure. Details often vary from project to project depending on the type of Client and the nature of the project. A detailed procedure that attempts to cover all projects is not therefore considered appropriate.

1.4   Quantity Surveyors may be appointed directly by a Client or as part of a multi-disciplinary team. The RICS recommends that the quantity surveying appointment is made directly by a Client so as to ensure that independent financial advice is made directly to that Client by the Quantity Surveyor.

1.5   The Guide provides a basis for the appointment of a Quantity Surveyor so that those concerned are clear about:
- the services being requested and/or offered
- the terms and conditions of the contract
- the fee payable and the method of payment.

A Client and his Quantity Surveyor should set out clearly their requirements in their agreement so that the services to be provided and the conditions of engagement are certain. It is necessary for a Client to set out his requirements with the same clarity as when seeking tenders from contractors on construction projects. It is now compulsory for Members of the RICS to provide written notification to their Client of the terms and conditions of the appointment. This documentation is intended to form a good basis upon which this certainty can be achieved and is recommended for use between the Client and his Quantity Surveyor.

2.   Notes on use and completion of documents

2.1   **Form of Enquiry**
The Form of Enquiry sets out the details of the services a Client wishes a Quantity Surveyor to provide and should be attached to the Form of Agreement and identified as belonging to it.

2.2   **Form of Agreement and Terms of Appointment**
The Form of Agreement should be completed and signed only when the services, fees and expenses have been agreed between a Client and his Quantity Surveyor. The

Form of Agreement states the names of the parties, their intentions and their arrangement.

The names and addresses of the parties should be inserted, a brief description of the project given and any site identified. If the Form of Agreement is to be made as a simple contract it should be signed by both parties and the date entered. If it is to be executed as a Deed the alternative version should be used. See notes *1 and *2 on page 40.

3. When to appoint a Quantity Surveyor

3.1 In order that maximum benefit can be gained from his skills a Quantity Surveyor should be appointed by a Client as soon as possible in the life of a project, preferably at the inception of a scheme, so that advice can be provided on:
- the costs of the project so that a realistic budget can be set at inception and cost management can be applied throughout
- the procurement method best suited to the requirements of the Client
- the implications of the appointment of other consultants and contractors.

3.2 It is recommended that a Client and his prospective Quantity Surveyor should meet and discuss the appointment before an agreement is reached, unless the services of the Quantity Surveyor are to be restricted only to some of those from the range available and shown in the Form of Enquiry.

4. How to select and appoint a Quantity Surveyor

4.1 Detailed guidance on the selection and appointment of chartered surveyors is given in the RICS publication *A Guide to Securing the Services of a Chartered Surveyor*. Chapters 2, 3 and 4 also provide useful information on preparing a brief for a Client's requirements, producing tender and contract documentation, organising competitions and evaluating offers.

4.2 Methods of selecting a Quantity Surveyor include:
- ***Selection based on existing knowledge***
  A Client may select and then appoint a Quantity Surveyor using existing knowledge of that Quantity Surveyor's performance and reputation. This knowledge may arise from a previous working relationship or be based on the recommendation of others
- ***Selection from a panel maintained by a Client***
  A Client may maintain a panel of Quantity Surveyors. He will have records of their experience which will enable him to make his selection and appointment
- ***Selection from an ad hoc list produced by a Client***
  If a Client is unable to make an appointment based on knowledge or reputation or by selection from a standing panel it may be more appropriate for an ad hoc list to be prepared.

4.3 Whichever of the above methods of selection is used it is important for the selection criteria to include the following:
- the financial standing of the Quantity Surveyor under consideration
- the experience, competence and reputation of each Quantity Surveyor in the area of the project/skill being considered so that selection is made using comparable standards between firms
- the ability of each Quantity Surveyor to provide the required service at the relevant time.

There is no one correct way to use competitive tendering as a basis for appointment and no single way of complying with legislation. It is important, however, that the procedure is always fair and open. Where legislation means that competition is compulsory, reference should be made to Clause 4.8 below and any other guidance available.

4.4   If competition is to be used in the selection process the following should be borne in mind:
- a Client should choose between the various methods of competition from either open, selective or restrictive lists, or single- or two-stage tenders, according to the complexity of the project which is to be the subject of competition
- the basis of selection can be on quality, competence or price, or a combination of all three. Whichever basis is chosen it must be clearly stated in the documentation inviting interest in the commission
- it is recommended that price is never regarded in isolation, as will be clear from the detailed guidance set out below.

4.5   To ensure that any competition is well organised the key ingredients required are that:
- specification of the service required is clear
- definition of the skills and competencies required to deliver the services is clear
- criteria on which offers will be evaluated will be made available with the tender documents
- any weighting to be applied to skills, competencies and price is made available with the tender documents
- each stage of the tender process is documented and the procedures for selection and invitation to tender match the requirements of the commission.

4.6   Every effort should be made to ensure that contract documentation is complete. If circumstances change to the extent that criteria are altered all tenderers should immediately be advised and given the opportunity to respond and confirm a willingness to continue.

4.7   **Private contracts**
In the case of private contracts there is no upper or lower limit to the number of private sector firms that may be invited to tender, nor formal rules as to their selection. Nevertheless, the RICS recommends that not less than 3 and not more than 6 firms are invited to submit proposals.

4.8   **Public contracts**
In the case of public sector contracts Compulsory Competitive Tendering rules and European Union rules, together with relevant Treasury regulations and DETR guidance, need to be followed. More information is available in the RICS publication *A Guide to Securing the Services of a Chartered Surveyor*. Chapter 2, pages 3 to 6, provides details on regulations but it is emphasised that current requirements should always be verified before seeking public sector offers.

5.   Specifying the quantity surveying service and determining the fee options and expense costs

5.1   It is emphasised that the fee for a project can either be negotiated, sought as a sole offer or sought in competition. The following considerations may apply to any of the methods of selecting a Quantity Surveyor and determining his fee in relation to the services to be provided.

5.2   When fee quotations are to be sought from more than one Quantity Surveyor it is of paramount importance that the enquiry and/or the submissions relate precisely to the same details of service(s) required. Proper use of the Form of Enquiry should ensure that this is achieved. In particular, the services required should be specified in detail, by using the Schedule of Services provided and/or by adding or deleting any special services not listed or required in that Schedule.

5.3   Information provided by a Client in an offer document should include, as a minimum:
- the complete scope of the project
- a full and precise description of the quantity surveying service(s) to be provided

- the terms and conditions which will apply, preferably the Form of Agreement and Terms of Appointment contained in this Guide, together with any further requirements that will apply
- the anticipated time scales that will apply, both for the quantity surveying service and for the project
- information on the inclusion or exclusion of expense costs
- the basis of the fee upon which the offer is being invited or offered including:
  - where a fee submission is to deal separately with different components of the service, the way in which any components will be evaluated in order to give comparable totals for selection purposes, and
  - wherever a percentage is to be quoted by a Quantity Surveyor, the definition of the total construction cost to which that percentage is to be applied
- provisions for stage or instalment payments
- where the nature, size, scope, time or value of the project or of the quantity surveying service(s) are likely to vary, the method(s) of appropriately adjusting the fee.

5.4　In determining the basis of the services and the fees required the following should be considered:
- where quantity surveying services are incapable of precise definition at the time of appointment, or where they could change substantially, enough information should be contained in an agreement to enable possible variations in those services to be negotiated
- where services are likely to be executed over a particularly long period, or where the service and/or the project might be delayed or postponed, the method and timing of any increase(s) in the fees should be stated
- the basis of the fees to be offered might be one of, or a combination of:
  - a single percentage encompassing all the described services
  - separate percentages for individually defined components of services
  - a single lump sum encompassing all the described services
  - separate lump sums for individually defined components of services
  - a time charge with either hourly rates quoted or a multiplier or adjustment factor to be applied to a specified definition of hourly cost.

5.5　Where the nature or scale of the project warrants it Quantity Surveyors may be invited to:
- explain in outline their proposed method of operation for the project, and/or
- demonstrate their ability to provide the services required from their own resources, and/or
- state the extent of partner/director involvement, and/or
- name the key personnel to be allocated to the project with details of relevant experience.

5.6　**Fee options**

Before offering any fee proposal a Quantity Surveyor will need to evaluate the costs of carrying out the service being offered. Options for charging fees are given below and may be used alone or in combination.

5.6.1　*Percentage fees*

This method of charging fees is appropriate when a construction project is reasonably straightforward and the quantity surveying service can be clearly defined but the exact amount of the total construction cost cannot be determined with much certainty.

In determining a fee, judgements need to be made by the Quantity Surveyor on the size of the project, its complexity, degree of repetition, method of procurement and contract arrangements. This method may be seen as a 'broad brush' way of assessment which sometimes may be vulnerable to market forces and their influence on contractors' tenders.

Fees are expressed as a percentage of a sum, which is invariably the total construction cost, for the provision of a defined service. This sum will generally be calculated from the value of all construction contracts and other items of work carried out directly by a Client on a project.

It is advisable to have a definition of total construction cost agreed between a Client and his Quantity Surveyor. Exclusions from the total construction cost should also be defined.

5.6.2 *Lump sum fee*
This method of charging fees is appropriate when a construction project is reasonably certain in programme time, project size and construction cost and the quantity surveying service can be clearly defined. A total fee is agreed for providing a defined service or amount of work. If appropriate, percentage-based or time-based fees may be converted to a lump sum fee once a project has become sufficiently defined.

If time, size, cost or circumstances of the project are significantly varied by more than specified amounts the lump sum fee may be varied, perhaps according to a formula contained in the Agreement. Otherwise the fee remains fixed. It should be borne in mind that a lump sum fee, whilst giving certainty to both parties at the start of a commission, may not always be appropriate unless the circumstances of the project remain significantly as stated at the time that the Agreement was signed.

5.6.3 *Time charge fees*
This method of charging fees is appropriate where the scope and/or the extent of the services to be provided cannot reasonably be foreseen and/or cannot reasonably be related to the cost of construction. It is often appropriate where open-ended services are required on feasibility studies, negotiation, claims consultancy etc. It is also a method that allows for additional or varied services to be provided, in addition to the provision of basic services quoted for in a fee agreement.

Fees are calculated from all the time expended on a project by partners/directors and staff and charged at rates previously agreed. The rates may be increased periodically to allow for the effects of inflation.

It is advisable to have previously agreed rates for grades of staff and partners/directors and methods of revising those rates periodically to reflect subsequent changes in salaries and costs. The inclusion of overhead allowances, generally including secretarial and administrative staff, within the rates needs careful calculation by the Quantity Surveyor. Principles for the reimbursement of the time involved also need to have been agreed in advance. Sometimes this method may appear to be open ended, perhaps with little incentive for working efficiently. Periodic review of the charges is important so that progress is monitored against budgets.

5.6.4 *Target cost fees*
This method is appropriate where time charge fees are the basis for the Agreement but a Client wishes to have a guaranteed maximum target for fees.

Fees are recovered on a time charge basis but a 'capped' or guaranteed target cost is agreed between the parties before the work is carried out by the Quantity Surveyor. If the target cost is exceeded then the Quantity Surveyor may not receive all of his costs, for instance part of his overhead allowances. If alternatively the total amount of the time charges falls below the budget cost then the Quantity Surveyor may receive an additional payment, a 'bonus' to reflect or share in the 'saving' to his Client. A formula for this should be agreed at the outset.

5.7 **Expense costs**
Expense costs are the costs to a firm such as the provision of cars, mileage-based payments to staff for travel, other travel costs, hotels, subsistence, meals, reproduction of documents, photocopying, postage and phone/fax charges, purchase costs of items

bought specifically for a project, expenses in connection with appointing and engaging site-based staff, exceptional time spent by staff in travelling outside of usual hours and/or beyond usual distances etc.

In any agreement on fees it is advisable to be clear about the inclusion or exclusion of any category of expense costs within the fee charges, to identify which expenses are chargeable and to have a machinery for adjustment where necessary.

5.7.1   *Recovering expense costs in fee arrangements*
Expense costs in fee bids and fee arrangements may be dealt with in a number of ways. Tender enquiries may prescribe the way required or there may be flexibility in how expense costs are included within the fee figures or shown separately from them. Three options exist for the recovery of expense costs in fee arrangements:
- ***Expense costs may be included within a lump sum fee***
  Expense costs of any variety can be assessed and included within a fee and not shown separately. The fee offer thus includes a lump sum for all expense costs. This is often referred to as a 'rolled-up' offer in that the costs have not been shown separately in the bid. Although expense costs have been so included it is often necessary to consider how any adjustment to those costs may be made if changed circumstances require. For instance, if travel costs have been included in a 'rolled-up' fee and much more travel becomes necessary, it may then be required to demonstrate the basis of travel expenses that had been included in the fee offer in order to agree an adjustment
- ***Expense costs may be converted to a percentage of the total construction cost of the project***
  An assessment is made of the likely expense costs that may be incurred and the amount is then converted into a percentage of the total construction cost. This percentage may be added to the percentage shown as a fee offer for the quantity surveying service or it may be shown separately. The relationship between construction costs, to which a percentage fee would be applied, and the amount of expense costs that will be incurred is often tenuous and this method should only be entered into after careful consideration by a Client and his Quantity Surveyor
- ***Expense costs may be paid as a separate lump sum***
  A lump sum can be calculated for expense costs and shown separately from any lump sum, percentage-based or time charge fee for the project. Whilst this method will give a Client certainty at the outset, provision should be made for adjustment by the parties if circumstances change.

5.7.2   *Constituents of expense costs and payment considerations*
If expense costs are not to be included in a lump sum, percentage-based or time charge fee they may be recovered by the Quantity Surveyor on the submission of the cost records. If this method is used it is important to establish how expense costs will be calculated and reimbursed to a Quantity Surveyor by his Client. There are three methods for this:
- ***Recovery of actual expense costs of disbursements incurred by a Quantity Surveyor with the authority of his Client***
  This category of cost would normally include items such as public transport costs, hotels and subsistence, and sundry expenses incurred, for instance, in obtaining financial reports on companies when considering prospective tender lists, or in establishing a site office
- ***Recovery of expense costs for in-house resources provided by an organisation***
  This would include, for example, photocopying and the reproduction of tender and contract documentation. The amounts due under this category of costs are not always as clearly demonstrable as the costs referred to in the previous category. It may be helpful to set up an agreement between the parties that allows the Quantity Surveyor to recover an amount in addition to the actual material costs incurred so that some staff and overhead costs can be recovered in addition to the basic costs

- ***Recovery of expense costs at market rates***
  This category is for resources provided by an organisation from its in-house facilities, for example photocopying or drawing reproduction, travel carried out by personnel using company cars etc. These costs would be recovered at what is agreed to be the market rate for the service provided.

5.8   **Implication of termination or suspension**
       If a project is terminated or suspended it may become necessary to consider the implications on fees and on expenses, for instance for staff, offices, cars, rented accommodation or leased equipment taken on especially for a project. It may be that some of these costs cannot readily be avoided if termination or suspension occurs and a fee agreement should contain provisions to allow adjustments to be made, particularly to lump sum, 'rolled-up' or percentage fees.

6.   Submission and comparison of fee offers and selection and notification of results

6.1   **Submission**

6.1.1   Clients are advised to invite fee offers only from firms of comparable capability and to make a selection taking into account value as well as the fee bid.

6.1.2   Where competitive offers have been sought, instructions on the submission of offers should be clear, giving the date, time and place for their delivery. Offers should all be opened at the same time and treated as confidential until notification of results is possible.

6.2   **Comparison and selection**

6.2.1   Competitive offers should be analysed and compared (including where there are different components of a fee evaluation, as referred to above). Comparison of offers should be on a basis which incorporates all the component parts of an offer in order to indicate the lowest offer and its relationship with other offers.

6.2.2   If two or more submissions give identical or very close results then it may be appropriate to apply a sensitivity test, namely to check the impact of possible or probable changes in the scope, size or value of the project on the fee bids.

6.2.3   In comparing offers it is advisable to weigh quality criteria against the offer price. Further detailed guidance is given in Appendix 10 of the RICS publication *A Guide to Securing the Services of a Chartered Surveyor*. It is usual to weigh quality of service criteria at a minimum of 60 per cent relative to price criteria at a maximum of 40 per cent.

6.3   **Notification**

6.3.1   Once a decision has been taken to appoint a Quantity Surveyor, the successful firm should be notified. Unsuccessful firms should also be notified of the decision and given information on the bids received (where appropriate this can be by the use of 'indices' which do not link the names of each firm to its offer). All notifications should be made in writing and be sent as soon as possible after the decision to appoint has been made.

7.   Confirmation of the Agreement between the Client and the Quantity Surveyor

7.1   The Agreement between a Client and his Quantity Surveyor should be effected by either:
       - using the Form of Agreement and Terms of Appointment contained in this Guide, with cross-reference to the Form of Enquiry, Schedule of Services and Fee Offer

- using a separate form of agreement, terms and conditions, with cross-reference to the services to be provided and to the fee offer
- a simple exchange of letters incorporating the information given above, making reference to the fee offer.

The 1996 Housing Grants, Construction and Regeneration Act ('the HGCR Act') introduced a right to refer any dispute to adjudication and certain provisions relating to payment. This documentation complies with the HGCR Act and includes the necessary adjudication and payment provisions. Other forms of agreement will need to comply with the HGCR Act or the adjudication and payment provisions of the Statutory Scheme for Construction Contracts will apply. An exchange of letters is unlikely to comply and the Scheme will therefore also apply to these.

8. Complaints handling and disputes resolution

8.1 Quantity Surveyors who are partners or directors in firms providing surveying services must operate an internal complaints handling procedure, which applies to disputes less than £50,000, under the RICS Bye-Laws. The RICS also sets a minimum standard of complaints handling, as laid out in its *Professional Conduct – Rules of Conduct and Disciplinary Procedures*. If the complaint cannot be resolved internally by the firm then the matter must go to final resolution by a third party. A reference to adjudication under the HGCR Act would be sufficient for the purposes of satisfying RICS regulations, pending any final resolution of the dispute at the end of the contract period. See also Clause 11 of the Terms of Appointment.

8.2 The HGCR Act introduced a compulsory scheme of third party neutral dispute resolution – which can occur at any time during the construction process – called adjudication. Any party may refer any dispute to an adjudicator at any time.

SECTION 2

Form of Enquiry

Schedule of Services

Fee Offer

Introduction

Use
The aim of this document is to help Clients to provide as much information as is available when seeking fee offer(s).

Issue and submission
The Client should enter:
- the information relating to the project in the Form of Enquiry
- the services required in the Schedule of Services, and
- those matters shown for completion by him in the Fee Offer

then send two copies of this document to the Quantity Surveyor(s), specifying the date, time and place for return of the offer(s).

The Quantity Surveyor should, having computed and inserted the fee figures (and any further information requested by the Client), complete, sign and date the Form and return it to the Client, retaining one copy for his own records.

Where any entries (other than the quoted fees) have been left for completion by the Quantity Surveyor, the Client should take careful note of such entries, particularly when considering competitive offers, in order that a fair comparison can be made.

Appointment
The formal appointment may be made by entering into the RICS Form of Agreement, incorporating the accepted Form of Enquiry, Schedule of Services and Fee Offer, specifying the project particulars and the services and quoting the fee(s). This should be signed by the Client and the Quantity Surveyor for identification purposes.

Form of Enquiry

The items set out below are those in respect of which information is important and details should be given. The further matters briefly set out in the grey text indicate information which should (where relevant and available) also be given. The user should not necessarily restrict information to that referred to in the grey text or attempt to cover all these points if they are not considered likely to have a material impact upon the quantity surveying services or the Quantity Surveyor's costs.

Where necessary, information should be expanded on further sheets which should be securely attached and cross-referenced to this form.

Extra sheets inserted are referenced as _____ to _____

(enter attachment page number)

1. Client

Name: _____

Address: _____

_____

_____

Telephone no: _____ Fax no: _____

Further information relating to this item:

1.1 Client's representative _____ *(address/telephone if different)*

_____

_____

1.2 Name and registered address of company entering into contracts with consultants/contractor if different

_____

_____

2. Project title and address *(if not known then list of sites being investigated)*

Title: _____

Address: _____

_____

_____

_____

Further information relating to this item:

2.1   Site abnormalities:

known _____

anticipated _____

2.2   Person to contact for site visit _____

2.3   Site area _____

2.4   Site plan _____

2.5   Means of identifying site _____

3.   General project description

Nature/purpose of building or works: _____

_____

_____

_____

_____

Number of separate buildings: _____

_____

_____

Floor area(s):

Name/description of building (list if several)	Number of storeys	Gross internal floor area m^2

Existing buildings, structures or works to be removed or which have been removed:

_____

_____

Further information relating to this item:

3.1   Availability of drawn information

3.2   Approved Client brief   *(if a brief is available it should be appended)*

3.3   Degree of repetition

3.4   Major specialist subcontracts   *(if known)*

4.   Project programme

Anticipated dates:

Scheme approval

Out to tender

Start on site

Practical completion

Details of any phases or sectional completion(s) required:

5.   Construction cost budget

VAT-exclusive budget for total construction cost at completion of the project:

£

Further information relating to this item:

5.1   Any available sub-division of budget

5.2   Statement of which costs are included in and excluded from budget

5.3   Phasing of expenditure   *(if appropriate)*

6. Project tender documentation

When the Quantity Surveyor is appointed at inception he is likely to be advising on some or all of these matters. Although it might not be possible to give precise details at this stage, all known or anticipated information should be given.

Method of procurement:

Lump sum*   Management contracting*

Prime cost*   Construction management*

Measured term*   Design and build*

Other* (state):

*(delete as appropriate)

Type of tender:

Competitive*   Firm price*

Negotiated*   Fluctuating price*

Two stage*

Other* (state):

*(delete as appropriate)

Nature of tender documentation to be produced by the Quantity Surveyor:
(a tick should be inserted in each column by the Client to indicate the specific tender documentation required)

	General building works	Mechanical and electrical services
Bill(s) of quantities: firm approximate		
Schedule of work		
Schedule of rates		
Quantified specification		
Prime cost schedule		
Other (specify)		

Further information relating to this item:

6.1   Form of contract   (if a standard form, state title/edition/revision or amendment)

7. Other consultants

Consultants appointed or proposed to be appointed by the Client to provide professional services in connection with the project:

Project manager _____

Architect _____

Structural engineer _____

Services engineer(s) _____

Planning supervisor _____

Lead consultant _____

Further information relating to this item:

7.1 Any other relevant consultants _____

_____

8. Professional indemnity insurance

Professional indemnity insurance is to be maintained by the appointed Quantity Surveyor in an amount of not less than _____ pounds (£ _____) for any one occurrence or series of occurrences arising out of any one event for a period of 6*/12* years from the date of practical completion of the project under the Building Contract.

(* delete as appropriate – the period should be 6 years for Agreements under hand and 12 years for those executed as a Deed)

9. Period of limitation

The period of limitation for the commencement of any action or proceedings against the Quantity Surveyor for breach of the Agreement shall be 6*/12* years from the date of practical completion of the project under the Building Contract.

(* delete as appropriate – the period should be 6 years for Agreements under hand and 12 years for those executed as a Deed)

10. Collateral warranties

Collateral warranties are not required*/are required and are to be executed and provided by the Quantity Surveyor as described below*:

Funders' Warranties executed on the Third Edition (1992) of the British Property Federation's Form of Agreement CoWa/F in favour of not more than _____ funders*

Purchaser/Tenant Warranties executed on the Second Edition (1993) of the British Property Federation's Form of Agreement CoWa/P&T in favour of not more than _____ purchasers and _____ tenants*

Clause 2 of the Forms of Agreement for Collateral Warranty will be deleted*

(* delete as appropriate)

The number of times the CoWa/P&T Warranty Agreements may be assigned, to be inserted or brought into effect at Clause 7:

| none* | once* | twice* | (* delete as appropriate) |

The warranties to be executed under hand*/as Deeds*   (* delete as appropriate)

Further information relating to this item:

10.1   Any amendments to the British Property Federation's Warranty Agreements

_____

_____

Note: the Quantity Surveyor is recommended to seek the consent of his insurers to giving such warranties.

Schedule of Services

Terms and conditions
The terms and conditions which apply to the Quantity Surveyor's appointment will be the RICS Form of Agreement and Terms of Appointment as set out in Section 3.

The Agreement

The Agreement will be under hand*/signed as a Deed*   (* delete as appropriate)

Quantity surveying services

The specific services required by the Client or offered by the Surveyor should be set out using the headings on pages 26-31. The services are listed under three categories:
- Category One: General services – those likely to occur on any project (pages 26-27)
- Category Two: Services particular to non-traditional methods of procurement (pages 28-29)
- Category Three: Services not always required in Categories One and Two (pages 29-31).

In respect of each item a tick should be inserted in the appropriate box by the Client or the Quantity Surveyor to indicate specific services required/offered. An unticked box shall be deemed to indicate that the service is not to be provided by the Quantity Surveyor.

Where necessary, items may be expanded to describe in more detail the specific services required/offered.

If any services are to be those of checking contractor-produced information rather than production by the Quantity Surveyor it should be so stated.

1. Category One: General services

The following services may be provided on any project, whatever its nature and whatever the method of procurement adopted.

☐ The following services shall, where relevant, also apply to environmental engineering services (mechanical and electrical engineering) if indicated by placing a cross in this box.

1.1 Inception and feasibility

1.1.1 ☐ Liaise with Client and other consultants to determine Client's initial requirements and subsequent development of the full brief

1.1.2 ☐ Advise on selection of other consultants if not already appointed

1.1.3 ☐ Advise on implications of proposed project and liaise with other experts in developing such advice

1.1.4 ☐ Advise on feasibility of procurement options

1.1.5 ☐ Establish Client's order of priorities for quality, time and cost

1.1.6 ☐ Prepare initial budget estimate from feasibility proposals

1.1.7 ☐ Prepare overall project cost calculation and cash flow projections

1.2 Pre-contract cost control

1.2.1 ☐ Prepare and develop preliminary cost plan

1.2.2 ☐ Advise on cost of design team's proposals, including effects of site usage, shape of buildings, alternative forms of design and construction as design develops

1.2.3 ☐ Monitor cost implications during detailed design stage

1.2.4 ☐ Maintain and develop cost plan, and prepare periodic reports and updated cash flow forecasts

1.3 Tender and contractual documentation

1.3.1 ☐ Advise on tendering and contractual arrangements taking into account the Client's priorities and information available from designers

1.3.2 ☐ Advise on insurance responsibilities and liaise with Client's insurance adviser

1.3.3 ☐ Advise on warranties

1.3.4 ☐ Advise on bonds for performance and other purposes

1.3.5 ☐ Prepare tender and contract documentation in conjunction with the Client and members of the design team

1.3.6 ☐ Provide copies of documentation as agreed

1.3.7 ☐ Advise on use and/or amendment of standard forms of contract or contribute to drafting of particular requirements in association with Client's legal advisers

1.3.8 ☐ Draw up forms of contract, obtain contract drawings from members of design team and prepare and deliver to both parties contract copies of all documents

1.4 Tender selection and appraisal

1.4.1 ☐ Advise on shortlisting prospective tenderers

1.4.2 ☐ Investigate prospective tenderers and advise Client on financial status and experience

1.4.3 ☐ Attend interviews with tenderers

1.4.4 ☐ Arrange delivery of documents to selected tenderers

1.4.5 ☐ Check tender submissions for accuracy, level of pricing, pricing policy etc.

1.4.6 ☐ Advise on errors and qualifications and, if necessary, negotiate thereon

1.4.7 ☐ Advise on submission of programme of work and method statement

1.4.8 ☐ Prepare appropriate documentation, if required, to adjust the tender received to an acceptable contract sum

1.4.9 ☐ Review financial budget in view of tenders received and prepare revised cash flow

1.4.10 ☐ Prepare report on tenders with appropriate recommendations

1.4.11 ☐ Advise on letters of intent and issue in conjunction with Client's advisers

1.5 Interim valuations

1.5.1 ☐ Prepare recommendations for interim payments to contractors, subcontractors and suppliers in accordance with contract requirements

1.6 Post-contract cost control

1.6.1 ☐ Value designers' draft instructions for varying the project before issue

1.6.2 ☐ Prepare periodic cost reports in agreed format at specified intervals including any allocations of cost and/or copies as requested by third parties

1.7 Final account

1.7.1 ☐ Prepare the final account

1.8 Attendance at meetings

1.8.1 ☐ Attend meetings as provided for under this Agreement

1.9 Provision of printing/reproduction/copying of documents and the like

1.9.1 ☐ Provide copies of documentation as provided for under this Agreement

2. Category Two: Services particular to non-traditional methods of procurement

These services relate to particular methods of procurement and contract arrangement and should be incorporated into the Agreement as required in conjunction with services from Categories One and Three of the Schedule.

2.1 Services particular to prime cost and management or construction management contracts

2.1.1 ☐ Obtain agreement of a contractor to the amount of the approximate estimate and confirm the amount of the fee for the contract

2.1.2 ☐ Prepare recommendations for interim payments to contractor based on contractor's prime costs

2.1.3 ☐ Adjust the approximate estimate to take account of variations and price fluctuations

2.1.4 ☐ Check the final amounts due to contractors, subcontractors and suppliers

2.2 Services particular to management and construction management contracts

The terms 'management contracting' and 'construction management' mean contractual arrangements where a firm is employed for a fee to manage, organise, supervise and secure the carrying out of the work by other contractors.

2.2.1 ☐ If required, assist in drafting special forms of contract

2.2.2 ☐ Prepare tender documents for the appointment of a management contractor or construction manager

2.2.3 ☐ Attend interviews of prospective contractors or managers

2.2.4 ☐ Obtain manager's agreement to contract cost plan and confirm amount of manager's fee

2.2.5 ☐ Assist in allocation of cost plan into work packages

2.2.6 ☐ Assist in preparation of tender and contract documents

2.2.7 ☐ Price tender documents to provide an estimate comparable with tenders

2.2.8 ☐ Review cost plan as tenders are obtained and prepare revised forecasts of cash flow

2.2.9 ☐ Prepare periodic cost reports to show effect of variations, tenders let and prime costs

2.2.10 ☐ Check the final amounts due to managers, contractors, subcontractors or works contractors and suppliers

2.3 Services particular to design and build contracts – services available to a Client

2.3.1 ☐ Draft the Client's brief, in association with the Client and his designers

2.3.2 ☐ Prepare tender documents incorporating the Client's requirements

2.3.3 ☐ Prepare contract documentation, taking into account any changes arising from the contractor's proposals

2.3.4 ☐ Prepare recommendations for interim and final payments to the contractor, including compliance with statutory requirements of the 1996 Housing Grants, Construction and Regeneration Act

2.3.5 ☐ Assist in agreement of settlement of the contractor's final account

2.4 Services particular to design and build contracts – services available to a contractor

2.4.1 ☐ Prepare bills of quantities to assist in the preparation of a contractor's tender

2.4.2 ☐ Prepare alternative cost studies to assist in determining the optimum scheme for a contractor's submission

2.4.3 ☐ Draft specifications forming the contractor's proposals

2.4.4 ☐ Assist with specialist enquiries in compiling the contractor's tender

2.4.5 ☐ Measure and price variations for submission to the Client's representative

2.4.6 ☐ Prepare applications for interim payments

2.4.7 ☐ Agree final account with Client's representative

2.5 Services particular to measured term contracts

2.5.1 ☐ Take measurements, price from agreed schedule of rates and agree totals with contractor

2.5.2 ☐ Check final amounts due to contractor(s)

3. Category Three: Services not always required in Categories One and Two

These services should be incorporated into the Agreement in conjunction with services from Categories One and Two of the Schedule as required. Where points are left blank, the Client and/or the Quantity Surveyor should specify their own service as required.

3.1 Bill of quantities

3.1.1 ☐ Provide bills of quantities for mechanical and engineering services

3.1.2 ☐ Price bills of quantities to provide an estimate comparable with tenders

3.2 Cost analysis

3.2.1 ☐ Prepare cost analysis based on agreed format or special requirements

3.3 Advise on financial implications as follows:

3.3.1 ☐ Cost options of developing different sites

3.3.2 ☐ Preparation of development appraisals

3.3.3 ☐ Cost implications of alternative development programmes

3.3.4 ☐ Effect of capital and revenue expenditure

3.3.5 ☐ Life cycle cost studies and estimate of annual running costs

3.3.6 ☐ Availability of grants

3.3.7 ☐ Assist in applications for grants and documentation for these

3.3.8 ☐ Evaluation of items for capital allowances, grant payments or other such matters

3.4 Advise on use of areas and provide:

3.4.1 ☐ Measurement of gross floor areas

3.4.2 ☐ Measurement of net lettable floor areas

3.5 Provide advice on contractual matters affecting the following:

3.5.1 ☐ Entitlement to liquidated and ascertained damages

3.5.2 ☐ Final assessment of VAT

3.5.3 ☐ Opinion on delays and/or disruptions and requests for extensions of time

3.5.4 ☐ Consequences of acceleration

3.5.5 ☐ Assessment of the amount of loss and expense or other such matters and if instructed carrying out negotiations with contractors to reach a settlement

3.6 Provide value management and value engineering services as follows:

3.6.1 ☐ *(state)* _____

3.6.2 ☐ *(state)* _____

3.7 Provide risk assessment and management services as follows:

3.7.1 ☐ *(state)* _____

3.7.2 ☐ *(state)* _____

3.8 Adjudication services

3.8.1 ☐ Provide services acting as an adjudicator in construction disputes

3.8.2 ☐ Provide services in connection with advising the Client in relation to active or threatened adjudication proceedings

3.9 Provide services in connection with arbitration and/or litigation as follows:

3.9.1 ☐ *(state)* _____

3.9.2 ☐ *(state)* _____

3.10 **Provide services arising from fire or other damage to buildings including preparing and negotiating claims with loss adjusters as follows:**

3.10.1 ☐ *(state)* _____

3.10.2 ☐ *(state)* _____

3.11 **Provide services to a contractor in connection with negotiation of claims as follows:**

3.11.1 ☐ *(state)* _____

3.11.2 ☐ *(state)* _____

3.12 **Project management**

Project management services are available from Quantity Surveyors and are set out in detail (together with a Form of Agreement and Guidance Notes) in the RICS publication *Project Management Agreement and Conditions of Engagement.*

Clients are referred to the *Project Management Agreement* if the service is mainly for project management. This section is intended to be used if ancillary project management is required to a mainly quantity surveying service.

Provide project management services as follows:

3.12.1 ☐ *(state)* _____

3.12.2 ☐ *(state)* _____

3.13 **Provide programme co-ordination and monitoring services as follows:**

3.13.1 ☐ *(state)* _____

3.13.2 ☐ *(state)* _____

3.14 **Provide planning supervisor services as follows:**

3.14.1 ☐ *(state)* _____

3.14.2 ☐ *(state)* _____

3.15 **Provide information for use in future management and/or maintenance of the building as follows:**

3.15.1 ☐ *(state)* _____

3.15.2 ☐ *(state)* _____

3.16 **Any other services not listed elsewhere in the Form of Enquiry:**

3.16.1 ☐ *(state)* _____

3.16.2 ☐ *(state)* _____

3.16.3 ☐ *(state)* _____

Fee Offer

When seeking fee submission(s) the Client should indicate the basis of fees, leaving the Quantity Surveyor to insert percentages or amounts appropriate to that basis.

1. Percentage or lump sum fees

Where fees are quoted as percentages the percentages shall be applied to the total construction cost at completion of the project.

Where fees are quoted as lump sums and the total construction cost at completion of the project differs from the budget figure set out in the Form of Enquiry by more than _____ per cent (or if the project or the quantity surveying services are significantly changed) the lump sum fees shall be correspondingly adjusted by a fair and reasonable amount having regard to such difference.

Note: the Client should normally insert the percentage in the paragraph above.

The total construction cost of the project shall comprise the actual amounts payable to the contractor(s) and subcontractor(s) for constructing and/or managing the construction of the project. This includes any fluctuations, work carried out directly by the Client which would normally be included in a building contract and the cost of any items provided by the Client for installation by the contractor. This excludes Value Added Tax, any loss or expense payable to the contractor(s) (if dealt with on a time charge basis) and any liquidated damages recoverable from the contractor(s) by the Client.

Where single percentages or lump sums are required for pre- and post-contract services, the Client (or where the submission is generated by a single Quantity Surveyor, the Quantity Surveyor) should strike out the boxes relating to components of service and fee.

In both sets of columns where there is provision for percentage or lump sum entries, the Client should indicate whether percentage or lump sum fees are requested, by deleting the relevant part of the fee column not required.

The basis of charging fees shall be as set out below:

	Fee		Component of service	Fee	
	Percentage %	Lump sum £		Percentage %	Lump sum £
Pre-contract services as defined in the Schedule of Services			Inception and feasibility		
			Cost advice		
			Tender and contractual documentation		
			Tender selection and appraisal		
Post-contracts services as defined in the Schedule of Services			Interim valuations		
			Cost advice		
			Final account		
Other services required *(state)*					

2. Time charges

The Client should delete the whole of either (A) or (B) below.

Note: where a partner/director does work which would normally be done by a member of staff, the rate charged shall be that of an associate or, if not applicable, a senior surveyor. Time spent by a partner/director on general administrative duties is not chargeable.

Where time charges are used as the method of payment for services, these shall be calculated on the hours actually expended by the relevant personnel:

EITHER

(A)   at the following hourly rates:

Partner/director   £ _____

Associate   £ _____

Senior surveyor   £ _____

Surveyor   £ _____

Junior surveyor   £ _____

Other *(state)*   £ _____

with adjustments to the above rates made annually in accordance with changes in the Retail Price Index from the date of the fee offer.

OR

(B)   at the hourly cost of the individual involved plus _____ per cent.

A member of staff shall include technical and supporting staff and a partner/director doing work normally done by technical staff, but shall exclude secretarial staff or staff engaged upon general administration.

The hourly cost shall be calculated by taking the annual cost for the member of staff of:

1.   salary and bonus but excluding expenses

2.   employer's contributions payable under any pension and life assurance schemes

3.   employer's contributions made under the National Insurance Acts, the Redundancy Payments Act and any other payments made in respect of the employee by virtue of any statutory requirements, and

4.   any other payments or benefits made or granted by the employer in pursuance of the terms of employment of the members of staff

and dividing the total by 1650.

3. Expenses

The method of charging expenses shall be as set out below.

Expenses are either chargeable in addition or included in the quoted fees as indicated below. In respect of each item a tick should be inserted in the appropriate column by the Client.

	Item	Chargeable in addition	Included in quoted fees
1.	Production of originals and copies of typed or printed tender and other documents If included in quoted fee state number of copies of tender documents to be supplied: _____ copies Additional copies of tender documents will be charged at: £ _____ per page		
2.	Photocopying (other than in preceding item)		
3.	Travelling (including mileage for car travel)		
4.	Hotel and subsistence costs		
5.	Others (specify)		

The basis of charging expenses where not included in the quoted fees shall be:

EITHER

(A)   at net cost plus _____ %

(B)   by lump sums, being:

pre-contract   £ _____

post-contract   £ _____

OR

(C)   by percentage, being:

pre-contract _____ %

post-contract _____ %

4. Instalment payments

Fees and other charges shall be paid by instalments as follows:

Stage of service completed (or date or other criteria)	Instalment payment (enter amount or basis of computing the same - including how expenses are to be incorporated)

5. Interest

Interest shall be paid to the Quantity Surveyor on fees due and payable but remaining unpaid 28 days after invoicing, the rate of interest being:

per cent per annum above LIBOR (London Interbank Overnight Rate)

6. Value Added Tax

All fees and other charges are exclusive of Value Added Tax, the amount of which shall be invoiced by the Quantity Surveyor and paid by the Client at the rate and in the manner prescribed by law.

7. Confirmation of fee offer

I/We offer to provide the quantity surveying services set out in the Schedule of Services hereof and on the basis specified therein, relating to the project information set out in the Form of Enquiry hereof, for the fees and other charges.

* set out above
* set out above and expanded on attached pages   to _____

(delete as appropriate)*

Signed: _____ Quantity Surveyor

Capacity in which signed: _____

For and on behalf of: _____

Address: _____

_____

_____

_____

This is the Form of Enquiry, Schedule of Services and Fee Offer referred to in the Agreement.

Dated: _____

Signed: _____ Client

Signed: _____ Quantity Surveyor

Form of Agreement

Terms of Appointment

Form of Agreement

THIS AGREEMENT is made the   day of   year

BETWEEN   ('the Client')

of

and

('the Quantity Surveyor')

of

The Client intends to proceed with

('the project')

at

('the site')

This Agreement relates to and shall be deemed to include the whole of the Form of Enquiry, Schedule of Services and Fee Offer, applicable to the project as so certified by the parties to this Agreement, together with the attached Terms of Appointment.

The Client hereby appoints the Quantity Surveyor in respect of the project to provide the services specified in the Schedule of Services and the Quantity Surveyor agrees to provide them.

The law in   and the jurisdiction of

the Courts in   apply to this Agreement

IN WITNESS whereof this Agreement was executed as a Deed and delivered the day and year first before written [*1]

by the Quantity Surveyor

by the Client

AS WITNESS the hands of the parties the day and year first before written [*2]

Signed by or on behalf of the Quantity Surveyor

Signed by or on behalf of the Client

Note: *1 and *2 are alternatives – delete as appropriate.
*1 is for use when the Agreement is to be executed as a Deed.
*2 is for use when the Agreement is to be executed under hand.

Terms of Appointment

1. Introduction

1.1 The Quantity Surveyor shall provide the services with reasonable skill, care and diligence.

2. Client's obligations

2.1 The Client shall supply such information to the Quantity Surveyor at such times as is reasonably required for the performance of the services.

2.2 The Client shall notify the Quantity Surveyor in writing of any agent appointed to act on behalf of the Client and of any change or dismissal of the agent.

2.3 The Client shall notify the Quantity Surveyor in writing of any instruction to vary the services.

3. Assignment and subcontracting

3.1 Neither the Client nor the Quantity Surveyor shall assign the whole or any part of this Agreement without the consent of the other in writing. Such consent shall not be unreasonably withheld.

3.2 The Quantity Surveyor shall not subcontract any part of the services without the consent of the Client in writing.

4. Payment

4.1 The Client shall pay the Quantity Surveyor for the performance of the services the fees and charges in such instalments as are set out in Clause 4 of the Fee Offer. All fees and charges under the Agreement are exclusive of Value Added Tax which if due shall be paid concurrently in addition. The 'due date for payment' shall be 7 days (see Clause 14.3 below) after the date of the submission of the invoice. The Quantity Surveyor when submitting his invoice shall on each invoice confirm the basis on which the stated amount is calculated.

4.2 The 'final date for payment' shall be 21 days after the due date for payment. Payment shall be made no later than the final date for payment.

4.3 The Client must, not later than 5 days after the due date for payment, give to the Quantity Surveyor written notice stating the amount which the Client proposes to pay and the basis on which that amount is calculated. Where no such notice is given the amount to be paid is that stated in the invoice.

4.4 Where the Client intends to withhold payment of any amount either stated in the Quantity Surveyor's invoice or in a written notice given by the Client under Clause 4.3 above, the Client must give written notice to the Quantity Surveyor not later than 5 days before the final date for payment, stating the amount to be withheld and the grounds for withholding payment.

4.5 Any amounts due to the Quantity Surveyor under this Agreement which remain unpaid by the Client after the final date for payment shall bear interest at the rate stated in Clause 5 of the Fee Offer.

4.6   In the event that the Client is in default over payment of amounts at the final date for payment and no notice of intention to withhold payment from such amount has been given under Clause 4.4 above, the Quantity Surveyor may suspend performance of any or all of the services. This right is subject to the Quantity Surveyor first giving the Client not less than 7 days' written notice of such intention and stating the grounds for suspension. The right to suspend performance shall cease when the Client makes payment of the amount due. Any such period of suspension shall be disregarded for the purposes of contractual time limits previously agreed for the completion of the services. Such suspension shall not be treated as a suspension under Clause 8 below.

4.7   The Quantity Surveyor shall notify the Client in writing as soon as it becomes reasonably apparent that any work additional to the subject of this Agreement will be required.

4.8   Where the Quantity Surveyor is involved in additional work because of:
•   changes in the scope of the works, and/or
•   changes in the programme of the works, and/or
•   changes instructed to the services, and/or
•   the commencement of adjudication, arbitration or litigation
the Client shall pay to the Quantity Surveyor additional fees calculated (unless otherwise agreed) on the time charge basis in Clause 2 of the Fee Offer.

5.   Professional indemnity insurance

5.1   The Quantity Surveyor is required to comply with the regulations of the Royal Institution of Chartered Surveyors in respect of the maintenance of professional indemnity insurance. He shall use reasonable endeavours to take out and maintain such professional indemnity insurance above RICS limits, provided that it is available at commercially reasonable rates, as defined by reference to an amount and for a period in Clause 8 of the Form of Enquiry. Such insurance shall be with an insurer who is listed for this purpose by the RICS.

5.2   The Quantity Surveyor shall on the written request of the Client provide evidence that the insurance is properly maintained.

5.3   The Quantity Surveyor shall immediately inform the Client if the insurance referred to in Clause 5.1 above ceases to be available at commercially reasonable rates in order that the best means of protecting the respective positions of the Client and the Quantity Surveyor can be implemented.

6.   Copyright

6.1   The copyright in all documents prepared by the Quantity Surveyor in providing the services shall remain the property of the Quantity Surveyor. Subject to payment by the Client of the fees properly due to the Quantity Surveyor under this Agreement the Quantity Surveyor grants to the Client an irrevocable non-exclusive royalty-free licence to copy and use the documents for any purpose related to the project.

6.2   The Quantity Surveyor shall not be liable for any use of the documents for any purpose other than that for which they were prepared and provided by the Quantity Surveyor.

7.   Warranties

7.1   As and when requested by the Client the Quantity Surveyor shall provide the collateral warranties required under Clause 10 of the Form of Enquiry, provided insurance cover is available in accordance with Clause 5 above.

8. Suspension and termination

8.1 The Client may suspend performance by the Quantity Surveyor of all or any of the services by giving 7 days' written notice to the Quantity Surveyor. If the services have been suspended for a period of more than 12 months either party may terminate the Agreement, by giving written notice to that effect.

8.2 The Client may terminate the appointment of the Quantity Surveyor under this Agreement by giving 7 days' written notice to the Quantity Surveyor.

8.3 Where the services have been suspended by the Client and the Agreement has not been terminated, the Client may, by giving reasonable written notice to the Quantity Surveyor, require the Quantity Surveyor to resume the performance of the services.

8.4 If the Client materially breaches its obligations under this Agreement the Quantity Surveyor may serve on the Client a notice specifying the breach and requiring its remedy within 28 days, and if the Client thereafter fails to remedy that breach within that period the Quantity Surveyor may terminate this Agreement by given written notice to the Client.

8.5 If either party:
- commits an act of bankruptcy or has a receiving or administrative order made against it, and/or
- goes into liquidation, and/or
- becomes insolvent, and/or
- makes any arrangement with its creditors

the other may suspend performance of the services or may terminate the appointment by giving written notice to the Client.

8.6 These rights are in addition to those granted to the Quantity Surveyor under Clause 4 above.

9. Consequences of suspension and termination

9.1 If performance of the services has been suspended under Clause 4 or Clause 8 above or the Agreement has been terminated pursuant to the provisions of Clause 8 above:

a) the Client shall pay the Quantity Surveyor any instalments of the fees due to the Quantity Surveyor up to the date of suspension or termination together with a fair and reasonable proportion of the next following instalment commensurate with the services performed by the Quantity Surveyor

b) unless the Agreement has been terminated by the Client because of a material breach by the Quantity Surveyor the Client shall pay the Quantity Surveyor within 28 days of written demand the consequential costs necessarily incurred as a result of the suspension or termination.

9.2 Termination of the Agreement shall be without prejudice to the rights and remedies of the parties.

10. Complaints

10.1 In the event that the Client has a complaint in respect of the performance of the Quantity Surveyor's services under this Agreement, without prejudice to any other remedy available under the Agreement, he shall be entitled to have access to the complaints handling procedure maintained by the Quantity Surveyor, written copies of which should be available on request from the Quantity Surveyor.

11. Disputes

11.1   If a dispute arises out of this Agreement the Client and the Quantity Surveyor shall attempt to agree a settlement in good faith. The internal complaints procedure mentioned in Clause 8.1 of Selection and Appointment Advice should facilitate this for disputes less than £50,000.

11.2   If the dispute is not thus resolved either the Client or the Quantity Surveyor may at any time give notice to the other in writing that he wishes to refer the dispute to an adjudicator, provided the contract is in writing and/or is not with a residential occupier. The person who is to act as the adjudicator shall be agreed between the Client and Quantity Surveyor within 2 days of such notice having been given or, failing agreement, be a person appointed by the President or Vice-President of the Chartered Institute of Arbitrators within 5 days of such notice having been given. The referring party shall refer the dispute in writing to the adjudicator within 7 days of such notice having been given.

11.3   The adjudication shall be conducted in accordance with the Construction Industry Council Model Adjudication Procedures current at the time of entering into this Agreement. Clause 30 of the Construction Industry Council Model Adjudication Procedures shall be amended to add the following sentence:

"No party shall be entitled to raise any right of set-off, counterclaim and/or abatement in connection with any enforcement proceedings".

11.4   The adjudicator shall act impartially and may take the initiative in ascertaining the facts and the law.

11.5   The adjudicator shall reach a decision:

a) within 28 days of the referral of the dispute to the adjudicator, or

b) within 42 days of the referral of the dispute to the adjudicator if the referring party so consents, or

c) in a period exceeding 28 days from referral of the dispute to the adjudicator as the Client and the Quantity Surveyor may agree after such referral.

11.6   The adjudicator is not liable for anything he does or omits to do in the discharge or purported discharge of his functions as adjudicator unless the act or omission is in bad faith. Any employee or agent of the adjudicator shall be similarly protected from liability.

11.7   The decision of the adjudicator shall, subject to the provisions of Clauses 11.8 and 11.9 below, be binding until the dispute is finally determined by arbitration either under the contract or as part of the Quantity Surveyor's internal complaints procedure for disputes less than £50,000.

11.8   The Client and the Quantity Surveyor may agree to accept the decision of the adjudicator as finally determining the dispute.

11.9   If the Client or the Quantity Surveyor is dissatisfied with the decision of the adjudicator then:

a) the dispute may be determined by agreement between the parties, or

b) the dispute may be referred at the instance of either of the parties to be determined by an arbitrator in accordance with Clause 12 below.

12. Arbitration

12.1   Any dispute arising under this Agreement, including those for more than £50,000 and/or those where adjudication would not apply, may be referred at the instance of either of the parties to be determined by an arbitrator. The person who is to act as an arbitrator shall be agreed between the parties within 28 days of the one giving written notice of his wish to refer the decision to an arbitrator or, failing agreement at the end of that period, shall be a person appointed by the President or Vice-President of the Chartered Institute of Arbitrators at the instance of either party. The arbitration shall be conducted in accordance with the Construction Industry Model Arbitration Rules current at the time of entering into this Agreement.

13. Liability

13.1   The liability of the Quantity Surveyor shall be limited to such sum as it would be just and equitable for the Quantity Surveyor to pay having regard to the extent of the responsibility of the Quantity Surveyor for the loss or damage suffered on the basis that all other consultants, the contractor and any subcontractors who have a liability shall be deemed to have provided contractual undertakings to the Client on terms no less onerous than those applying in the case of this Agreement and shall be deemed to have paid to the Client such sums as it would be just and equitable for them to pay having regard to the extent of their responsibility for such loss or damage.

13.2   The liability of the Quantity Surveyor shall be limited to the amount of the professional indemnity insurance required by virtue of Clause 5.1 above.

13.3   No action or proceedings for any breach of this Agreement shall be commenced by either party after the expiry of the period of limitation (specified in Clause 9 of the Form of Enquiry).

14. Notice

14.1   Any notice to be given under this Agreement shall be in writing and delivered by hand or sent by recorded delivery post to the party at the address shown in this Agreement or to such an address as the other party may have specified from time to time by written notice to the other.

14.2   Such notice shall be deemed to have been received on the day of delivery if delivered by hand and otherwise on the next working day.

14.3   Where under this Agreement an act is required to be completed within a specified period of days after or from a specified date, the period shall begin immediately after that date. Where the period would include a day which is Christmas Day, Good Friday or a day which under the Banking and Financial Dealings Act 1971 is a bank holiday that day shall be excluded.